ACCEPTANCE

ACCEPTANCE

A COLLECTION OF PROSE ABOUT
LIFE, LOVE, AND LEARNING

CHARLENE FOX

STEWART PRESS PUBLISHING
300 SOUTH MEDIA GROUP

NEW YORK

This book is presented as a collection.

ISBN-13: 978-1-957596-13-6

First Edition January 2023

Book Design & Cover Design: Indie Author Solutions
Published by Stewart Press Publishing

Stewart Press is an imprint of 300 South Media Group

For those who have experienced pain in their past and still believe in the promise of healing.

Acknowledgements

I want to express my love and gratitude to my best friend of over 20 years, who has always been my constant confidant and who loves me without judgment. I love you so much Tricia.

To those who follow me on social media, those to whom my words resonate, thank you for allowing me into your world daily.

I appreciate those in the writing community who have shared my words on your platforms. It gave me more confidence in my writing and means everything.

A special thank you to my good friend Jay Long who gave me an outlet to share my thoughts in ink. Thank you for always believing in me and helping me to believe in myself.

And finally, to my family. I love you and only want to make you proud.

— Charlene

Table Of Contents

THE PAST   1

    What Abuse?   3
    The Masquerade   6
    Can I?   9
    The Dance   10
    No Stopping You   12
    You Are Enough   13
    Over-Qualified   14
    Forgive   16
    Connect the Dots   17

THE PAIN   19

    Angels Fall   21
    Anywhere But Here   22
    Broken Remains   23
    Darkness Steals My Light   24
    Eyes Swollen   25
    Final Hours   26
    Empty Tomorrows   27
    Give Me the Night   28

Gray Skies   29
I Pour My Heart Out   30
Left In Pieces   30
Thought Love Would Be Enough   31
If All You Did Was Cry   32
Impenetrable Fortress   33
It's Called Self Care   34
Live To Feed Another Day   35
Lost Moments   36
Minute By Minute   37
New Shoes   38
Night Terror   39
Open Book   40
Open Season   41
Outside Looking In   42
People Change   43
Rush   44
Shattered Remains   45
She Will Love Only Him   46
Steal Your Joy   47
Suffocating Sadness   48
The Duller the Ache   49
The Heart Always Wins   50
Pills Are Looking Good Right Now   51
The Queen   52
The Wreckage   53
Unrequited Love   54

Wait For You   55

Waiting For Inspiration   56

Waiting With Open Arms   57

What If's and Could've Been's   58

What Is Grief?   59

What Love Is Not   60

When Sadness Consumes Me   61

Women Like Me Are Rare   62

Yet To Be Determined   63

You Opted For a Phone Screen   64

You   65

It Would Lead to Heartache   66

Love Is Pain   67

Hear It From You   68

Each Exhale   69

Into the Abyss   69

Jaded   70

Swallowed Words   71

Her Love Was Denied   72

I Wish You Could See Me   72

Shattered Heart   73

Make the Effort   74

A Light Gone Forever   75

THE PROMISE 77

Fire Within 79
The Tide Turns 80
Goodbye Satan 81
Only In My Mind 82
Tell Me What I Need to Hear 83
It All Feels Right 84
Change Is Uncomfortable 84
Put Ourselves First 85
My Happily Ever After 86
Believe In Ourselves 87
I Welcome You In 88
Down the Drain 89
Baptized In Your Love 89
My Love Knows No End 90
Wanted 91
Slay Your Day 92
Top It Off 93
Ignite a Fire 94
Tomorrow 95
A Brand New Day 96
Surrender 97
Someone To Love 98
Taste of Heaven 99
Silent Song 100
Shine Again 100

Our Love Story   101

Pause   102

Silent Journey   103

She Feels She's Home   104

Pillar of Strength   104

Old Soul   105

Never Harden   106

My One   107

My Heart's Desire   108

Swim In Their Depths   109

Moonglow   110

My 11:11 Wish   111

Loving You   112

Sweet Secrets   113

Just Breathe   114

I'm Home   115

Paradise   116

I Love You   117

I Hand You My Heart   118

A Thief In the Night   119

Home   120

My Reverie   122

Heaven & Hell   123

Gypsy Road   124

Lips On Fire   125

I Want To Lay With You   126

For All of This   127

Fly High   128
Find Your Way   129
I Touch My Lips   130
He Held Her Tightly   131
Find Your Light   132
Faith In Humanity   133
It's Taboo   134
Everything Changes   135
Endless Love   136
Drunk On You   137
Darkness Falls   138
Dragon Slayer   139
Dear Diary   140
Closed Doors   141
Breathe   142
Bloom   143
Branding You Mine   144
Acceptance   145

ABOUT THE AUTHOR   146

Cleanse the Soul

We all sit in a darkened place looking for a way to cleanse the soul.
Standing strong and finding your own light, that is the ultimate goal.

To find yourself, is to find your light

THE PAST

The shame is real. You never thought it would be you, and you don't realize it is until it's too late.

What Abuse?

During my first serious relationship I had suffered physical abuse at the hands of who ultimately would be my fiancé. The first time he slapped me, he cried and begged forgiveness, vowing never to lay hands on me again. I gave him a pass believing he would be true to his word.

By the time I received my first punch, he had me so deep in debt that I needed his paycheck to help pay the rent. By the time there were so many bruises I couldn't leave the house, we were engaged. Somehow, I found the strength to kick him out. I had to file a personal protection order for my safety. He stalked me for seven years and attempted to kill me several times during those years. Only when I faced him in court did it all end.

Fast forward to my second abusive relationship. That relationship was verbally, emotionally and mentally abusive and lasted 14 years. He was also an alcoholic. Everyone saw it except for me. There was no physical abuse for which I was thankful, therefore to me abuse did not exist. But I was so wrong.

He would tell me who I could talk to, which were only his friends. He would not allow me to visit family, only his friends. He would tell me what to do, when to do it and how it should be done. What to wear, what to eat, when to speak. Without even knowing it, I had been brainwashed. To me that's what the mind fuck is. A narcissist will brainwash you, much like the leader of a cult.

Then there was the time he pulled me off the couch by my hair and proceeded to smother my nose and mouth because I wasn't interested in talking to him when he was drunk. Another mind fuck, I gave him a pass too.

Just shy of our 14-year mark, he told me he wished I would die on the table while I was getting ready to leave for surgery. That was it, the straw that broke the camel's back. I kicked him out at that very moment, had my surgery, came home and packed up all his shit the same day. That's when I knew that I was stronger than I thought.

We have an out from any abusive relationship. We have to know the signs of mental and emotional abuse. We are the ones that have to take care of ourselves in order to survive and live a happy life.

I have been dealing with my healing for several years. I am still a work in progress, but I have knowledge now that I didn't have then. Do your research, make a plan, save some money, pack a bag, and get out. You've got this! If I can do it, I know you can do it too.

The Masquerade

Sometimes it is easier to pretend we are someone that we're not. We may feel we have to impress a crush. We may do it to impress a potential employer. We may do it to feel better about ourselves. I could go on and on....

That is what I used to do. I always wore a fake smile. I would have to wear make up to hide the bruises. I always pretended to have fun when I was with friends or family.

I was so accustomed to wearing a mask so no one could see my pain. Even though I was dying inside, I couldn't let anyone see it, I could not let anyone know.

I wore my mask to hide from the shame and embarrassment of knowing I could possibly die at the hands of my abuser, but that I did not know how to find a way out.

I wore my mask in shame for spending 14 years with someone who stole my joy daily. A man who took the person that I was and said such awful things to and about me, that I no longer had 'life' inside.

My sparkle dimmed; my flame had blown out. I became a shell of who I was, a zombie, if you will. He did this in order to control me. Narcissistic asshole.

I could not allow my family or friends to worry about me. I did not want to be judged. It did not want to be belittled or berated. I had enough of that from the men who 'loved me'.

It was so much easier to wear the fucking mask. And it started to fit well. I used to think if people would have looked hard enough, they may have seen the pain in my eyes. But did I let them look at me long enough? Oh no, I would look past them and then walk away.

Perhaps they would notice the quiver of my chin every time I wanted to cry. Nope, I would simply turn my face away, fake a cough, and try to compose myself.

That is something that I have forgiven myself for. If I hadn't, I would not be where I am today. Healing has been an exceptionally long process and I've had many ups and downs. There have been many bumps in the road that I have had to travel.

I am NOT that person anymore. I was slowly able to take off that mask. Leave the ball better than when I arrived. I let the wrong men sign my dance card. I danced with the devil, and he thought he won.

But I proved him wrong. I showed him how strong I was. I showed him that I was more important than anything or anyone else. I showed him that my love for myself would keep me alive.

And the mask? It's just a reminder of where I've been and how I survived.

Can I?

Sometimes, when you've lived a life with trauma, you are terrified to love again. Every time I tried, I often did or said something to sabotage the relationship. I would find myself caring too much. I didn't want to fall too fast. I didn't want to be hurt again. It was self-preservation.

Facing the struggle of healing and finding myself again, I have found that I can genuinely have true feelings of love for someone. That I can voice these feelings to them and not want to run away from either the person or how I felt. Whether or not reciprocated, I feel good knowing I can release the words.

As human beings our hearts are made to feel love, accept love and to give love. As trauma survivors, it's our mind that struggles with the idea. Retrain your brain and remember that we are all worthy to be loved and cherished.

The Dance

We all want instant gratification - whether it's food, drugs, sex. We even want our relationships fast. That's not so easy when you're a victim of trauma. We feel so broken, and often ashamed, by how we've been treated. We feel worthless because we were told we were. We feel invisible because we've been ignored.

Yet we still want someone to love us, someone to hold us when we're sad, someone to show us that we matter. When we have those opportunities, we shy away. We're too scared, we don't want to chance it being another traumatic relationship.

There's a lot of work we need to do on ourselves, a lot of healing, reflection and soul searching. We also need to do what we can to make it easier for us to want a close relationship with someone. That's what's most important. That we heal ourselves before we jump into any type of relationship.

I think if you meet someone and there's an instant connection, that in time your hearts will intertwine, and love can prosper. But nothing can be forced, and we shouldn't try to force it.

Life's a dance, right? So, I'll sit this one out so when OUR song starts playing, he'll find me, and my feet won't be tired. Then we can dance together for eternity.

No Stopping You

For almost three decades I was told that I was worthless, that I wasn't enough, that no man would ever love me. It's taken several years of healing to realize that statement was wrong. I've slowly learned to love myself, scars and all, to know my worth and to 'not put myself on discount'. If we want someone to love us, we need to learn to love ourselves first. Once you do that everything changes. The way you see yourself changes; the way others see you changes. There is such a glow about you, it exudes from you. Once you find happiness in yourself there is no stopping you.

You Are Enough

For 13 years I believed what he said, that I was worthless, that I wasn't enough and that without him, no man would ever love me. It's taken several years of healing to realize that he was wrong. I've slowly learned to love myself, scars and all, to know my worth and to 'not put myself on discount'. If we want someone to love us, we need to learn to love ourselves first. Once you do that everything changes. The way you see yourself changes; the way others see you changes. There is such a glow about you, it exudes from you. Once you find happiness in yourself there is no stopping you.

You are enough, you always have been, and you always will be. Never let anyone tell you differently.

Over-Qualified

For years I was told that I was not worthy of any type of love in my life. I wasn't enough to make anyone happy, I didn't do enough to make anyone happy. The funny thing is that I have always been one to wear my heart on my sleeve. I have always been one to love without limits. I was the one that did so much to make other people happy.

When you are consistently told you're worthless you believe it. The people who tell you that strive on saying it so that you feel like you're nothing. Those who make us feel worthless only do it because they're weak. They do it because they feel worthless, and it makes them feel better to bring someone down to the level they are at.

It's only been the last few months that I've realized that I do have value in this world. I do add value to people's lives. That the people who told me I was worthless are the ones that were unworthy of me. If you woke up this morning, you're worthy. If you have children, you're worthy. If you have friends, you are worthy. We are the ones to set our value. Don't sell yourself short just to be with someone. We all have value in this world. We're all on this Earth for a reason. To allow someone to devalue us is not it!

Don't settle for less than the best.
You are indeed overqualified.

Forgive

That's something I can do when others commit a wrong against me. I never stopped to consider forgiving myself. Forgiving myself for allowing someone else to control what I did, when to speak, what I said, who I spent time with.

What an epiphany.

Today is the day. One of the last steps to healing. I think perhaps this is what I've needed to do for years in order to close that book and start a new one.
A fresh perspective, a whole heart and a desire to shine in this world. To live in the now without allowing triggers to steal my joy. To look back on my past and say 'thank you' because I'm becoming a better person for having lived there. And as I once read, 'there's no sense looking in the past. You didn't leave anything of value there'. So, here's to acceptance, forgiveness, and self-love. I deserve it and I've earned it.

Connect The Dots

Today I am grateful. I have an excellent job, a roof over my head, family, and great friends. Good friendships are hard to find and even harder to maintain.

There are some friends I haven't seen in years, yet when we see each other, we pick up where we left off like we just talked yesterday. Then there are the ones I've never met. Friends I've met online, other friends from companies I deal with at work.

Regardless of the length of my friendships, my life has most certainly been touched by them being a part of it. Embrace the people that come into your life and treat you with kindness and respect. May the ties that bind never be broken.

Remember to be kind. You never know what someone else is going through. Just one kind word or gesture could brighten the day of even the saddest person. Share a smile, even on your worst day, you will get so many in return. And in turn your mood will lighten and your whole attitude will improve.

And please, when you find a connection, that deep connection with someone, hold on to that friendship and never let it go. It's the universe changing the course of your life.

THE PAIN

It's buried deep and comes to the surface in waves.
Looking for release, the tears flow unchecked.

Angels Fall

There's a fire burning
a rage I can't control
the angels from above are fighting
the demons from below
my screams are getting louder
the angels give their all
my demons are much stronger
the angels had to fall

Anywhere But Here

I wanna be anywhere but here –
where you're not beside me
where you're not holding my hand
where you're not holding me close

I wanna be there –
where she sits beside you
where you're holding her hand
where you're holding her close

Broken Remains

All those things you said to me
All those words of love
The promise of a future
I believed the words you said
I hung on your every word

Such a fool was I
you left without warning
your promises were broken
You left my heart shattered
Just the pieces remain

Darkness Steals My Light

Even when I'm at my happiest,
of the blue sadness can overwhelm me.
No rhyme.
No reason.
I feel it from my head to my toes, that sinking feeling.
The flush.
It washes over me like a wave until the water flows
from my eyes.
It doesn't stop.
Darkness steals my light.
A constant battle but I always come out the victor.

Eyes Swollen

Eyes swollen from the rivers I've cried.
Red and burning like the fires from hell.
He doesn't know, would be even care?
Tossed aside like table scraps.
He hurt me, yet I'm to blame.

Thoughts of him burned into my memory.
Dreams that will never come true.
Like regret tattooed on my skin.
Like the fool I am, I wonder why.
I will always feel he was worth it.

Final Hours

I knew in my heart she was saying goodbye,
I could feel it the moment I woke up.
We were all there during her final hours,
But she knew it would be too hard for me.
So, she took her last breath when I was not in the room.
For that, I thank you Grandma.

Empty Tomorrows

In memory of Gwen

This COVID is a killer, it takes all it can get.
The young, the old, the middle aged.
The vaxed, the unvaxed,
It does not discriminate.
It takes husbands and wives, Mothers and Fathers.
Sisters and brothers. No family is left untouched
It takes them way too soon, their families can't
prepare
The shock sets in, their hearts are broken
Yesterday is a memory, today is the goodbye.
All that's left are empty tomorrows.

Give Me the Night

When the sun goes down the darkness in my heart
surrounds me like a shroud.
The sadness is overwhelming,
but I've learned to welcome it.
The tears fall, too many to count,
a river flowing down my cheeks.
Give me the night,
where the sad and lonely walk alone.
Out of sight, far from anyone's thoughts.
Where lonely hearts break continuously.
Gone are the days where hope leads to happiness,
where the sunrise welcomes a bright new day.
Yes, give me the night, where I can break and shatter,
forever alone.

Gray Skies

I feel the chill in the air, I feel it on my face.
The covers are pulled tight all around me.
Like a cocoon on this cold winter day
How I miss the summer, the sun high in the sky.
I look out the window.
The snow is coming. I see only gray skies.

I Pour My Heart Out

No one understands how hard it is to heal from any
type of abuse,
unless they've been through it.
This is why I pour my heart out in ink.
Someone reading my words knows exactly how I feel.

Left In Pieces

It hurt when you said goodbye
You thought I would never get over you
Yet here I am, stronger than ever before
My heart no longer left in pieces on the floor

Thought Love Would Be Enough

I wanted to give you everything.
I thought my love would be enough.
But now there is no longer a desire to hold you,
to taste you, to love you.
You ensured you put a stop to that with just four little
words.

If All You Did Was Cry

if all you did today was cry,
dry your eyes,
wipe your face,
and put on that smile,
then you did something right

Impenetrable Fortress

I am standing on the cusp of understanding,
waiting for the surrender among my chaos.
But the universe only laughs at me.
"You're almost there.
There's only one thing left to learn.
Don't let your heart get in the way, you will get hurt
every time."
Now its fortress has been reinforced and will forever
be *impenetrable*.

It's Called Self Care

When you try to hold on to him,
knowing you're causing your own heartbreak,
that's when you know it's time to let go.

When you never even had him,
despite the love you feel for him,
all you can do is say goodbye.

It's called self-care.

Live To Feed Another Day

There's just you and me, alone in a room full of
people, but you're the only one I see.
I come to you as if in a trance and you take my hand.
You lead me through dark hallways, up many dark
stairwells. Finally, we are at your lair, and you pull me
through the door.
I see the bed covered with red satin and I know what
happens next. You sense I'm nervous, so you squeeze
my hand, and say 'You've nothing to fear, this is just
the beginning.'
But it's not nerves my darling, it is excitement. I have
done this before. And when I nuzzle your neck and my
teeth sink into your flesh, a look of shock floods your
face. As I wipe the blood from my lips, I've only one
thing to say. 'Two can play your game, and I have lived
to feed another day.'

Lost Moments

All the times I could have spoken
Said exactly how I feel
But so afraid of your reaction
So before I lose the moment
And before I lose my nerve
Just let me say 'I love you'
Or let me take it to my grave

Minute By Minute

Minute by minute, hour by hour, day by day. That is how often I thought of you.

For months I gave all that I could. I gave what was left of my heart to you.

I would like to think that you knew that, just by the things I said.

They may have been only words to you, but those words were all that I could offer.

Those words came from the heart. From MY heart.

I'd like to think that you took those words and put somewhere safe.

Tucked them deep in your heart so you could hit replay repeatedly.

Hearing that you were loved. Knowing you were loved.

But then you felt so distant, you felt so far away.

And time goes by, the clock keeps ticking.

I am starting to feel an emptiness where you used to reside.

Knowing that you never felt the same, there is a sadness inside.

But if I had to do it all again, I wouldn't hesitate.

For knowing that I love you, lets me know that I'm alive.

New Shoes

The road of life can be a very arduous journey. We happen upon many things that can cause us sadness. When the road gets too tough, and we need a bit of traction to move forward, maybe it's time to buy a new pair of shoes. Leave our troubles behind us. Bury them deep so they can't catch up.

Night Terror

What started as a night terror,
Ended in a love story.....

In the midst of my slumber your demons come.
They hold me down while you begin your evil work.
As you cut through skin and bone, your face is
distorted in a sneer.
Your eyes so dark and evil, never leave mine. I stare
back at you so defiant.
As you take my heart from my chest you tell me it is
yours and yours alone. You run out the door, your
demons not far behind you.
You can keep it; it lost its beat long ago.
What you did not know is that my old broken,
bruised, and battered heart had been replaced. A new
heart beats in its place. One that you will never get
your hands on.
It beats for me alone, to share with who is deserving
of its worth.

Open Book

I exist with many chapters
I am a love story and a mystery
A nightmare and a fantasy
Your fingers turn my pages as each one is read

I captivate and excite you
I leave you anxious to know more
You bring each part of me to life
As you read one chapter after the next

Will your heart break or will you smile?
Will I be a victim or a survivor?
Will I be hated or loved?
Will I be judged or accepted?
My life is an open book but promise me this
You won't just see the cover

Open Season

It seems I've spent eternity trying to find out who I
am.
I'm not good enough,
I'm too loud,
I'm too quiet.
I'm too soft,
I have no strength.
So, I've been a chameleon, changing into who they
want me to be.
Never being who I am.
Each time killing a part of me.
I've believed the lies,
I've given my all for people who don't deserve me.
In my heart I know there's a purpose, something
wants to just break free.
So, take good aim,
it's open season.
Kill who you think I am,
I just want to be me!

Outside Looking In

Passing through the park, I see a happy couple. I see the smiles on their faces as they look lovingly into each other's eyes. I see the gentle caresses as they sit together on the bench. I see their fingers slowly entwined, one with the other. They look completely inseparable, completely in love.

When is it my turn? Why does it have to be I'm always on the outside looking in?

People Change

People change, I get it
Yet it wasn't some gradual pulling away
You changed overnight
Overnight
To always be there
Then suddenly you're gone
To feel so replaceable
Not knowing what I've done
It's like a punch in the gut
A punch which I won't recover

Rush

Too many times we meet someone we think is our soul mate.
We try to force our hearts to love instead of leaving it to fate.

And then one day we realize the love is not returned.
We end up with a broken heart, once again we just got burned.

We tell ourselves to try again, this time we'll wait and see.
So, what's the rush? slow down already. What's meant to be will be.

Shattered Remains

Some relationships just aren't good for us. Abusive
and narcissistic relationships change us.
Where we were once happy and filled with joy, we
become just a shell of who we once were.
All that's left are the shattered remains of our dreams
of a loving relationship.
We can find the strength to break free and that's when
the healing begins.
It does take years to find ourselves, re-learn to love
ourselves and feel our hearts beating once again.
I've been there and believe me, it's worth it in the end.

She Will Love Only Him

She stood by the window blankly looking out into her own thoughts.
Thoughts of her life with him.
Nights by the fire when the days were cold.
Relaxing on the beach on those hot summer days.
The nights always found them exploring each other's bodies.
Lips following hands, tasting each other in the most delicious ways.
But he's gone now. Taken too soon.
The sickness eating away at him slowly.
She will live with the memories.
He is irreplaceable.
She will love only him.

Steal Your Joy

There's a saying 'Don't let anyone steal your joy'....
I have realized that no one can steal our joy. We lose
our joy when something upsets us and especially
when someone hurts us. We allow the pain to control
us. But our joy comes back. It comes back from where
it's hiding behind our broken heart, our tears or both.
We just have to remember where we put it and lead it
back home.

Suffocating Sadness

I can't describe how I feel right now
It's a suffocating sadness
It's hard to breathe
With the heartache inside
The tears pool in my eyes
Yet cannot fall
Like frozen when they touch the air
Oh, how I wish my heart were that cold

The Duller the Ache

As spring approaches,
I welcome the days getting longer
The shorter the night, the less I dream about you
The less I dream about you, the duller the ache
The duller the ache, the quicker I will forget the love I
gladly offered you
The love you swiftly denied

The Heart Always Wins

Everyone has had a broken heart at some point in their life. We talk to people just hoping that by expressing our pain we will somehow feel better. People mean well giving advice and we really want to take it but the heart, well, it's the strongest muscle. The heart always wins. Feels what it wants. Hurts and heals how it wants. We just release the tears until it heals.

Pills Are Looking Good Right Now

The pills are looking good right now
The ones that help her sleep
In her own little world of happiness
Away from the pain so deep

She only needs a couple
And then she'll close her eyes
She'll find she's in a happy place
With nothing but blue skies

The grass is always lush and green
It tickles her feet and makes for smile
It really is so beautiful
It stretches out for miles

She's never felt such happiness
She loves just how it feels
But she knows when she awakens
The pain will still be real

The pills are looking good right now.....

The Queen

She is the queen that sits atop her throne.
We are merely her subjects.
We exist to do her bidding, follow her orders.
Decisions are not ours to make.
Her opinions are voiced freely as she rules with an iron fist.
She is our judge; she is our jury, and she is our warden.
Will she be our executioner?
She makes you feel small, makes you feel worthless.
Nothing we can do will gain us any value to her.
Doing this makes her feel stronger.
Be careful not to anger her.
Her tongue spews venom that cuts deep into your heart.
She'll hear you bleed out, cry for help, yet not bat an eye.
She does no wrong, she is the queen.
There are only two ways to escape.
Do we choose exile or wait for the day the throne is empty
to gain our freedom?
I have bled out.
I've no more to give.
I choose exile.

The Wreckage

Our life together was never perfect
But I tried to make it work
There were so many twists and turns
I knew we were heading for disaster
Now all that's left is the wreckage

Unrequited Love

With my heart wide open you found your way in.
Little did I know I would fall.
There is nothing like the painful sting
of unrequited love.

Wait For You

The nights are so long with you in my thoughts but
not in my arms.
So empty the bed where we used to lay.
So cold the sheets our bodies once made burn.
Lost in love, lost in each other.
The nights without you cause such an ache in my
heart.
Such an emptiness that only you can fill.
I'll wait for you until time stands still.
And will be ready when your love comes this way
again.
To warm my heart and fill my soul.
For just one more moment in time.

Waiting For Inspiration

I sit here, pen in hand, waiting for inspiration
looking for something to help the words form a
sentence
is there nothing left to inspire me?
do I write of love? No, that's for fairy tales and
I stopped believing in those long ago
do I write of passion? no that is something my life is
lacking
So, what does one do when their writing is blocked?
I will think of you
the one who makes me believe in love
the one who makes me believe in passion
the one whose kiss, I know, will set my soul on fire
the one whose arms will blanket me and keep me
warm
the one whose heart I long to possess

Waiting With Open Arms

She sits alone in a room staring at the walls
Trying to stop the pain she's feeling
But the tears rolled down her cheeks unchecked
Her heartache so real it steals her every breath
She wishes she could talk to him
To tell him how she feels
But when she gets the courage
She also feels the fear
She knows his heart is closed to love
That they are only friends
She knows if she says anything
That could be where the friendship ends
She'll hold her feelings close to her heart
His friendship is too much to lose
Hoping one day he'll change his mind
And she'll be waiting with open arms

What If's and Could've Been's

I have always questioned my past relationships.
Wondering why things didn't work out.
Regretting that some things did.
Then there was you. A breath of fresh air.
Just like Spring, I opened my heart to you.
Just like summer, I felt your warmth.
But with Winter came the cold.
The realization that there was no us.
That it was just you and it was just me.
Your heart was not invested, where mine was all in.
I hope you struggle with the what if's and could've
been's.
What if you opened your heart as I did?
What if you let me in as much as I did?
What if you gave of yourself as much as I did?
Knowing I loved you with all that I had.
And would protect you just as much.
You would have always been supported.
You would have always felt special.
You would have always known you were enough.
You would always be taking care of.
You would never feel alone.
How great our relationship could've been.
Had you only let me in.

What Is Grief?

Knowing your heart was never good enough
For someone else
Your love was never accepted
By someone else
That you will always be alone
Always questioning why

What Love Is Not

We'll date a hundred people before 'our one' comes
along.
From them we will learn what love is not.
Once you feel those red flags flying,
remember your worth and walk away.

When Sadness Consumes Me

When sadness consumes me,
Tears fall down my cheeks unchecked.
Creating an ocean at my feet,
One in which I'll surely drown.
When will my rescuer come,
And save me from this death?

Women Like Me Are Rare

You gotta be careful with a woman like me
When I tell you I love you, it's because I do
But when I feel used or taken advantage of,
Neglected or treated wrong
That's when I get quiet
And when I get quiet
That's a sure sign you're losing me
And when you're losing me
You'd better do something
You just may lose your forever
Because women like me are hard to find
Women like me are rare

Yet To Be determined

There is a storm raging inside
My mind wreaking havoc
The tears falling like rain
The anger inside spinning out of control
Like a tornado touching down
If only I could control The Tempest
Calm the winds
Stop the rain
Peace?
Yet to be determined

You Opted For a Phone Screen

When all was said and done
I reached out for your hand, and it was gone
there was nothing left
no friendship, no love, just cold indifference
instead of wanting what was pure and right in front of
you,
you opted for a phone screen and fantasy
so, who's really the loser here?

You

You are the one I think of before anything else
You are the one who makes me feel beautiful
You're also the one who makes me feel invisible
It will be hard, but I have to say goodbye
To the thought of you every morning
To say goodbye to...
YOU

It Would Lead to Heartache

When you extended your hand, I took it,
Not knowing where you would lead me.
It was a new feeling,
like someone genuinely cared.
Little did I know it would lead to heartache.

Love Is Pain

Love is pain and ecstasy commingled together forming a sweet taste on one's lips, until that sweet taste turns to bitter venom.

Hear It From You

I wanted to hear 'you're beautiful'
I needed to hear 'you're worth it'
I wanted to hear 'I've got you'
I needed to hear 'I love you'
But more than anything,
I longed to hear it from you.

Each Exhale

I close my eyes and breathe in deeply
Thoughts of you on my mind
Each exhale calls you name
Will you ever hear me?

Into the Abyss

All-encompassing sadness
pulling me into darkness.
Deeper and deeper
into the abyss I fall.
Surely this is death.

Jaded

I want to love again, I really do. And I want to be loved in return. I believe it's a natural human emotion. It's just hard when you've been hurt so many times. I wanted the dream - the loving husband, modest house, white picket fence. But at age 55 I think it's too late for me. The past has left me jaded. It's difficult for me to trust people. So, I accept that I will live out my days alone. I have my friends, they are enough. There is love there, there is trust there. It will have to be enough.

Swallowed Words

There is so much I want to say to you,
the words are stuck in my throat.
Do I take the chance?
Or do I keep silent yet again?
They say silence is golden,
but I just want to shout!
There has got to be a way to get them all out.
But I don't think you'll care
so, I'll keep them swallowed.
Maybe I can tell you 'I love you' tomorrow.

Her Love Was Denied

Her love was denied for far too long
So, her heart closed back into itself
Locked in a cage, it will forever be a prisoner
Never to be free to love again

I Wish You Could See Me

I wish you could see me the way I see you.
I wish you could love me the way I love you.
Maybe in our next lifetime.

Shattered Heart

When you care too much for someone
who doesn't feel the same about you,
you end up breaking your own heart.
How many times does mine have to
shatter before I finally learn?

Make The Effort

I'm just gonna say this…
If you want me in your life, make the effort.
It's a two-way street and I'm tired of driving both
directions while you sleep behind the wheel.
If you can't or won't make the effort
then I don't need ya.

A Light Gone Forever

all she knew all her life was pain
pain in her youth
pain in her adulthood
pain by her parents
pain in her relationships
but this would be the last
she lost her light for the last time
and as she forced the jagged edge through her wrists
the moon lost its glow
the stars fell silent
in tribute to a light gone forever

THE PROMISE

You look for the one that makes you whole.
You finally find yourself.
You finally find acceptance.

Fire Within

"Strike it." they said. "Light that match.
You only need the flame to touch the edge."
My life was on those pages,
my tears became the ink.
Each page was stained with every word written.
But the only way to let go of the past
was to light that match.
So I did.
The fire on the pages became
a fire burning within me.
I could finally say goodbye,
Goodbye to the painful past,
And hello to a brand new life.

The Tide Turns

We walk along the beach like lovers do,
The moon and the stars to light our way.
You pull me closer, and I feel the warmth of your
embrace.
Your arms feel like home, so welcoming, so strong.
As you hold me tighter,
I nuzzle your neck and breathe you in.
When your lips touch mine, my body comes alive,
As though hit with the crashing waves of the ocean.
I welcome the feeling, never wanting it to end.
And as the waves take me deeper under,
I welcome the baptism of your kiss.
Fully aware that just as the tide turns,
Your lips will soon leave mine.

Goodbye Satan

Letting go of my past is something that I need to do in order to find complete happiness within myself.
I want to soar yet can't with my past weighing me down. So goodbye. Get thee behind me Satan.
You have been evicted.
No more renting space in my head.
No more visits when I am weak.
YOU DONT LIVE HERE ANYMORE!

Only In My Mind

As I began to stir, I could feel his warm breath on my shoulder. Feeling the weight of his arm around my waist I snuggled in closer, to feel all the warmth he has to offer. It feels so nice to be this close to the one who owns my heart, and I don't want it to end. But I know if I open my eyes, it will all be gone, for it is only in my mind that he holds me. It's only in my mind that I am his. So, I'll lay here a little longer, eyes closed, pressed against his chest, outside of my reality.

Tell Me What I Need to Hear

Tell me what I need to hear
Tell me how I make your days a little brighter
Tell me that you smile when I cross your mind
Tell me that you imagine how I feel in your arms
Tell me that you think about how my lips might taste
Because I promise you;
this is how I think of you every day

It All Feels Right

With a quick kiss on my forehead, you rise.
I watch you walk away and admire the way you look.
I slowly roll over and inhale your scent on your pillow.
Just the way we are, it all feels right.

Change Is Uncomfortable

Acceptance, self-love, whatever holds you back....
change is uncomfortable, challenging, and hard as
hell. But it is necessary to become your best self.

Put Ourselves First

It was late this year that I learned to, and succeeded in, loving myself again. Slowly finding myself, I am starting to believe in myself again. I am fighting a winning battle and I am reaping the rewards.
I come first - selfish or not. I am my own priority, protecting my heart is my priority.
Loving myself is my priority.
We all need to put ourselves first! If we don't, we take the chance of becoming someone else.
And that person just won't do. I, for one, will never again lose who I really am for another person.

My Happily Ever After

I look back on my life and I see a lot of disappointment.

I see a lot of heart ache.

I wonder why it was never my turn.

I wonder why God never gave me my 'one'. The one who could love me for me. The one who would keep my heart a treasure. The one who would build with me rather than tear me down. My happily ever after. As I try to be everything to everyone, I wish someone would want to be that for me. I wish someone wanted to be my 'one' to accept me and to love me, just as I am.

Maybe someday.

Believe in Ourselves

Our mind is our own worst enemy. It rules us in every thought, every action, every reaction. But we can be our best healer, if we start to think of the happy things in our lives rather than what causes our sadness. Let's flip that switch and take control for a change. Let's make our own happiness in this new life we are creating for ourselves. Let's believe in ourselves and live our best life.

I Welcome You In

My head is spinning,
as if drunk by the scent of you.
The sensual words whispered in my ear,
I am beyond aroused.
The intensity of our kiss,
a passion burning out of control.
Knowing what comes next,
I can't help but wet my lips
and welcome you in completely.

Down the Drain

None of us are ever promised a great life. Our life is what we make it. It's time I make my life count. It is time to step into that shower, scrub off all that pain, and let all the heartache flow down the drain.

Baptized In Your Love

The moment you took me in your arms
I knew you were my savior
and I just wanted to be baptized in your love

My Love Knows No End

Where the night ends and the day begins
is a beautiful transition.
Every morning the same feelings come over me.
There is such a peace, such a calm, such tranquility.
I love when I feel this way. It is a whole new
beginning.
There is so much to me that people don't know.
So much that, like the moon, I keep hidden.
But the sweetest of my secrets is this…
I love with every fiber of my being
and my love knows no end.

Wanted

With covered eyes and my body bound I feel your
weight as you sit on the bed.
I feel the feathers touching my skin and they feel like
the kisses of ten thousand butterflies.
Your fingers trail behind them following the same
path. Their touch so soft, yet in control, as though
writing words upon my skin. Sentences that lead to
my tenderest spot. Without hesitation your fingers
glide into my treasure and my body moves with
a primal rhythm. When I am close to rapture you
stop. You want to hear it; you want to hear me beg.
After all, it is my role.
'Don't stop. Write your book. You're all I've ever
wanted.'

Slay Your Day

Every morning when you wake up
Take a look in the mirror
Shoulders straight, head high
Tell yourself how beautiful you are
You've got this!
Slay your day!

Top It Off

It's been a long day and it's nice to be home
I sit as you pour two glasses
The whiskey warms my throat, and it feels so smooth
But your words in my ear are smoother
As you take my glass to top it off, you see the heat in
my gaze
Taking my hand, you set the glasses down
and lead me to our haven
Forget the whiskey, your what I crave
Let me drink you up for hours

Ignite a Fire

You ignite a fire inside me with just a simple look.
I feel the embers burning so deeply in my soul.
All I want to do is love you,
write a chapter in my book.
I can't help it; these feelings are just something I can't
control.

Tomorrow

Passion........with you it is a passion that I simply can't deny.

Contact........skin on skin, tongues at play, your fingers slowly tracing down my ribcage.

Spreading....my legs wider as you find your place of refuge.

Trembling...with every thrust you hit the spot and my body comes alive.

Shudder........convulsing, spasms, having a rhythm all our own.

Holding........spent and tired we drift off to sweet slumber.

The love.......we share, the love we made. We'll share it again tomorrow.

A Brand New Day

We have been given the gift of a brand-new day. Breathe it in. May you find peace and acceptance with yourself and everyone you cross paths with. Be kind to each other, encourage each other and hold each other up. If one falls, we all do.

Surrender

Then one day it happens, you're standing on the cusp.
You see the door in front of you, but you are afraid to
take that step.
You take that deep breath in and have that long
exhale.
You straighten your spine and lengthen in your neck.
You square your shoulders and hold your head up
high.
You've had an awakening, a renewal of spirit, a
rejuvenation of the mind.
You have found freedom.
You grasp the handle and turn the knob.
You have surrendered to the need.
You know with that first step over the threshold,
you're walking into a new life.

Someone To Love

All we really want is someone to love
someone who loves us in return
Who will see our flaws
And still think we're perfection
Someone who accepts us as we are
Someone to catch us when we fall
A safety net to cushion the landing
A place where we feel safe
A place where our minds can rest
A heart we can call home

Taste of Heaven

Lying with you now,
our lips just inches from each other.
The weight of your body on mine.
The warmth of your skin covering me like a blanket.
I smell the whiskey on your breath,
and I can't wait to taste it.
With a mind of their own, my hands gently cup your face,
my eyes giving my thoughts away.
Your mouth finally devours mine and the taste is exhilarating.
In that instant I have finally found my taste of heaven.

Silent Song

When I see your name on the caller ID
When I see your name on text message
When I hear you say my name
My heart sings a silent song

Shine Again

We are two stars in the universe
Separate yet joined together
As my light dims you lend me yours
Until I can shine again

Our Love Story

We met in the summer. It was an unexpected instant connection. Some call them soulmates; others call them twin flames. We were fine calling each other friend.

We both had loved and lost, we both had scars on our hearts. But you wouldn't know that if you saw us together. We were so carefree, laughter we hadn't known in years drifting all around us.

By the fall our friendship had changed. We started to see each other differently. We stared at each other longer than usual. We would find any excuse to be together.

Then one day it happened, underneath the oak tree by the river. You looked at me, rubbing your thumb along my cheek. 'I have always loved you' you said as you brought your lips to mine.

Our fate was sealed that day.
Our hearts had finally found home.

Pause

Pause. Breathe deep. It's not that bad
He just found a crack and chipped away at it
Until it was large enough for him to crawl through
With all his strength he started tearing down the walls
It feels good, doesn't it? To allow someone in?
To give his heart a home?
And though the walls are down
Your heart is still protected
Because now he holds it in his hands

Silent Journey

With the sun peeking through the clouds and the
sound of the waves,
I find a peace that helps me think.
I think about who I was, who I am, and who I am
becoming.
My mind has found clarity. I am at peace.
I've said goodbye to chaos and self-destruction.
I'm learning to live in the now.
A now with endless possibilities.
My journey has been a long one, but I'm finally at a
place where I am in control.
Of my emotions and of my future.

She Feels She's Home

She sits alone, closing her eyes,
just to see his face one more time.
This is when she feels she's home.

Pillar of Strength

Pillar of strength,
rising to salvation,
honoring yourself in courage.
The strong will never fall.

Old Soul

I wasn't looking when I found him,
I was just at the right place at the right time
and the connection was immediate.
When I brought him home, he was so unsure,
but my kindness did not go unnoticed
Before I knew it, he was on my bed purring so loud.
He found his place right on my pillow
and that's where he'd always stay.
He was more than just my pet; he was my companion
and we rescued each other that day
He was my Atticus, a tender old soul.
He was loved beyond measure.

In memory of Atticus 1/1/2007 - 2/17/2021

Never Harden

Another new day,
another chance for freedom.
Another day onward and forward to be the best
person I can be.
Another day of hope that each day will be better than
the last.
A future where positivity lives,
and I can live alongside it.
Where I can breathe it in freely, every day.
To never let my heart harden by the burdens of the
past.
Today I say ENOUGH.
I am taking back control.

My One

I have always searched for, but never found my 'one' in a relationship. A connection where there is friendship, a bond that should exist with every couple. One where there is mutual respect. Where there is kindness, empathy, compassion, and more importantly, LOVE.

A love that can be felt with just a touch and can be seen with just a look. One where you feel the attraction, the desire, you feel the longing. The one where just a look is a caress. Where just a touch claims me. A love where not just your heart, but your soul, your entire being, belongs to someone else. A love that takes you beyond the limits of heaven when you blissfully become one.

I will find him.
He will find me.
My One

My Heart's Desire

In my darkest day a stranger's hand reached out for mine.
How was I to know you'd be the one I was longing for?
You opened my heart, knocked down my walls
You have become my heart's desire

Swim In Their Depths

If you got close enough to stare deep into my eyes
would you like what you see? Would you see the ache?
Would you see the love? Would they mirror yours?

If I could get close enough to stare deep into your eyes
I would swim in the depths of them
Swim in their warmth, swim in their kindness,
swim in their love.

Lay with you on their sun kissed shores.
Watch the clouds roll in with each touch.
Hear the thunder when we start to kiss.
Feel the rain on our flesh as our passion grows
stronger.
Feel the heat of the lightening when we become one.
And when the tidal wave comes, we ride it till it's over.

Then when the storm is over and rest covers your face,
I look at you and plead. Please don't close your eyes.
If you do my reverie is over, and I just don't want it to
end.

Moonglow

I think I see you standing there, in the shadow of the
Moons glow.
I've been hoping, making wishes on shooting stars,
that you would find me.
Did she send you down to hide in her shadows to keep
watch over me?
Or are you here to take me on a wild ride through the
universe?
From the stars to the sun, through the Milky Way and
her moon beams?
Did she send you here to keep my secrets?
The ones I only share with her?
Don't stay in the shadows,
come out where I can see you.
Come out where I can see your glow,
where I can see your shine.
Tell me Moonchild because now that I've seen you,
I know that you are mine and I never want you to go.

My 11:11 Wish

You are the miracle I was longing for
My 11:11 wish granted
The mate to my soul, looking for its own
We were two stars in the universe
Separate, yet somehow joined together
Both feeling there was something more
Something missing to make us whole
Then by fate our stars aligned
The impact so great it lit up the sky
The sun smiled
The moon beamed
The planets bowed
The stars danced
Celebrating our union
I am yours
You are mine
The one I've waited my whole life to find
Finally
The other half of me

Loving You

You're my first thought in the morning and my last thought at night.

It's the moments in between where our love grows.

Stolen kisses watching the sunrise, walking hand in hand.

Hugs that warm me from head to my toes.

The midnight strolls along the beach, keeping every seashell we had the luck to find.

I think of all the love we share and how blessed I am to call you mine.

Sweet Secrets

In my heart there is a longing.
I feel it pulling me closer.
Closer to the one who stays in the dark.
The one who stays in the shadows.
Where my sweet secrets must remain.

Let me stay in the darkness with you.
Tell you of my secrets.
You're the only one who needs to know.
Learn of my every valley, every curve.
Feel my petals as they open to you.
Taste my sweet secret while I moan your name.

Before I am found out, cover my mouth with yours.
While our souls feed only off each other.
And when the craving is too much, brand me yours.
Fill me deep with your desire until our thirst is
quenched.

In my heart there's a longing.
I feel it pulling me closer.
Closer to the one who stays in the dark.
The one who stays in the shadows.
Where my sweet secrets must remain and forever you
will stay.

Just Breathe

Too often we sit alone and wallow in self-pity.
Our painful memories in the forefront,
our lives on the back burner.
Not allowing ourselves to be who we are meant to be.
We need to be accepting, loving,
and nurturing of ourselves.
We need to get out of our heads and bury the past.
We have remarkable futures waiting for us,
there for the taking.

Just breathe.

I'm Home

The way you touch me so tender and gentle
Like I'm a delicate bowl in a China shop
You know I've been hurt before
So, you take your time to show me your different
As you take me in your arms
You whisper words endearing
Making me feel beautiful
Making me feel cherished
Making me feel loved
Making me feel I'm home

Paradise

I stand before you naked and wanton,
waiting for you to reach out for me.
You just stare, no words, no instructions.
You simply lick your lips.
Placing a blindfold over my eyes,
you finally take my hand.
I feel the cold steel as it closes around my wrists.
As I gasp you whisper in my ear,
'Don't be afraid, I won't hurt you.
Let me take you to paradise.'

I Love You

I have a great ability to love,
being empathetic does that to a person.
I love harder than most which is why I hurt so deeply.
If I tell you I love you,
please know it is one of the most genuine,
and hardest things, that I will ever say to you.
Please don't take it for granted.

I Hand You My Heart

And when I tell you I love you and I hand you my heart, take it and keep it in a safe place.
Make sure you treasure it, it's the only one I have.
It's been broken, it's extremely fragile, and it's meant only for you.
The one I've waited my whole life to find.
The other half of me.

A Thief In the Night

To feel the warmth of your body pressed against mine
is what I dream of every night.
When I close my eyes, you come to me.
I see you looking at me with so much desire.
And as you hide in the shadows,
I reach down and touch myself.
As I part my lips, you lick yours.
The devil in your grin, yet I watch you.
Fingers pleasuring, pressure on my bud,
I start to reach my climax.
You come from the shadows
To take all that can be yours.
Forcing my arms above my head,
You plunge into me completely.
So slick is the ride, so deep the thrust,
It doesn't take long for each of us to find rapture.
And then you're gone....

A thief in the night.

Home

I finally found him, the other half of me.
My soulmate, my twin-flame.
The one who called to my soul, and I heard you.

You too were looking for your second half,
the missing part that makes you whole.
Alone too long, you were ready to find your 'one'.
You felt the tug on your heart,
leading you in my direction.
The universe had spoken, your wish had been
granted.

Your soulmate, your twin-flame.
The one who called to your soul, and you heard me.

The tenderness in your eyes say the words your mouth
is afraid to speak.
You gently place your palm over the place where my
heart rests, unbeating.
With one kiss you breathe it back to life.

When I touch you, you feel the love in my fingertips,
without a word having to be spoken.

The tenderness in my hands matches the tenderness
in my heart.
You know my love is true and I will never hurt you.

Your hands are strong enough to move mountains
and they move me in a way no other man could.
With each touch from you, I feel your strength, and it
makes me stronger.
When you hold me in your arms, I know I belong
there.

I know that I am safe.
I know that I am home.

My Reverie

Late at night when it's dark and quiet,
that's when it all begins.
With my back to you,
I feel your warm breath so close to my ear,
whispering words of adoration and love.
I roll over smiling and nuzzle closer to you.
Gently touching your chest, my fingertips running
over the goosebumps left in their wake.
You grasp my hand and as our fingers intertwine so
do our legs.
You tenderly kiss my forehead and as I open my eyes,
I realize, the reverie is over.
It was only just a dream.

Heaven & Hell

When I think of hell
I think of my past
The beatings, the belittling
The pain

When I think of heaven
I think of you
Your touch
Your love
Happiness

Us together
A miracle
A blessing
Sent from above

Gypsy Road

I've always been a loner
Always taken the road less traveled
Finding my way alone
Solitude guides me
Like a gypsy walking alone
I walk to the beat of my own drum
My journey has shown me dark places
But it's also taken me to the light
Each heartbeat pulling me closer to you
My journey is not over
I walk where the spirits guide me
Till I find you, a love that's true

Lips on Fire

I was burning hot, yet it wasn't a fever.
It only happened when he was around.
Sensing my need, he came to the rescue.
Reaching into my panties,
with a single touch he felt my heat.
My lips on fire just waiting to be extinguished.

I Want To Lay With You

I want to lay with you
In my bed
Under the blankets
Your arms around me
Holding me close
Our legs intertwined
A sensual play
My head on your chest
Hearing your heartbeat
Feeling my breath
So warm on your skin
Our hearts start beating as one
Our breathing in unison
This is intimacy
This is what I want
I just want to lay with you

For All of This

When I am weak, you give me strength
When I am sad, you bring me joy
When I'm upset, you give me comfort
When I am stressed, you bring me peace
For all of this - I thank you

Fly High

Take me, take me by the hand
Take me to heights I've never imagined
Let's soar through the clouds
Far beyond the rainbow
Let's pass through the star dust
And far beyond the moon's beams
Make me fly so high
Far away from this place
Far away from this world
And all its hate
Where all we feel is love
Where all we have is each other

Find Your Way

You've been searching for so long,
trying to find you're place.
Your heart open yet empty,
wanting someone to fill the space.
You see me walking down the street,
and your heart begins to leap.
You feel as though we met before,
that you saw me in your sleep.

When our eyes meet you catch your breath,
your dreams became reality.
There was no reason to look further,
you found your way to me.
I also had a space to fill,
my heart had been broken too.
The universe had spoken, I found my way to you.

We knew we would share forever,
with our first tender kiss.
Blissfully aware nothing would be better than this.
Together our hearts had found their home,
finally they were aligned.
I'll be your Queen; you'll be my King.
Forever, for all time.

I Touch My Lips

Closing my eyes, I think of you and touch my lips,
Remembering the warmth of yours on them.
They are still tender to the touch
Rubbing my tongue over the lower,
I feel the small swell
Caused by my teeth when you start to bring my body
alive.
The fire in me rises when I think of how you touch me,
How you cause my body to shudder.
Knowing it will only be you
And the daydreams I have in your absence.

He Held Her Tightly

He held her tightly,
relishing the softness of her skin,
the scent of her.
They had made love for so long that night,
in all the ways that lovers do.
He could still taste her wet lips on his,
and again, he was getting aroused.
He would let her sleep.
When she awoke, he would make her his,
Again.
Knowing tomorrow,
she would be gone forever.

Find your Light

As dark as the night can be there is always light in the morning.
It reminds me of the healing process after emotional abuse.
You start out in a dark place and barely recognizable. With self-love and acceptance, you find your light, where everyone notices you and loves who you've become.

Faith in Humanity

There's always someone who has it worse than we do. If you are talking to someone, really look at them, look into their eyes when you talk to them, when you say hello and ask how their day was. Eyes can't hide pain when you're suffering. If they say they're OK, ask them again. And if you have just a flicker of doubt, tell them you're there for them if they need to talk.

Open that line of communication. Give somebody a reason to want to open up. They may feel they have no one to talk to who would understand. Let them know they do.

Kindness goes a long way. It is free to take and free to give. So please be kind, you never know if you might be saving a life.

It's Taboo

I know I'm not supposed to, I know it's taboo and you are off limits to me, but I couldn't help myself.

My heart beats with life and with a deep desire that needs to be sated. So, I thought of you tonight.

I thought of your hands on me, touching my body in the warmest and wettest places. I thought of your mouth on mine, our tongues caught up in a dance all their own.

I thought of your possessing me, from the swell of my breasts to the petals of my flower. And when you entered me, my legs wrapped around you tightly so as to never let you go.

Just one night to feel you, all of you, become one with me. The rapture was bliss and I'm still warm from the sensation.

And as my mind rests, I know I will always dream of this. Knowing that you are loved.

Everything Changes

Trying to drag myself out of the pit of my despair,
Is so frightening it leaves me gasping for air.
But I keep reaching knowing the surface is near,
Finally out, everything changes, and I'm still here.

Endless Love

The first time I saw you, you looked at me with questioning eyes.
Neither of us was very sure about the other.
We were only able to see each other every other weekend, but the more time we spent together the more we became friends.
That first time you grabbed my hand, I remember gasping.
You looked up at me with a smile so wide I couldn't help but smile back and give your little hand a squeeze.
That is the exact moment you stole my heart, and I knew my love would be endless.
I knew then you weren't just his little girl, you were mine too.

Drunk On You

My head is spinning, as if drunk by the scent of you.
The sensual words whispered in my ear;
I am beyond aroused.
The intensity of our kiss,
a passion burning out of control.
Knowing what comes next, I can't help but wet my lips
and welcome you in completely.

Darkness Falls

It's in the darkness when I think of you
When I imagine you are with me
Where I lay with my head on your chest
And you rub my back so softly
Where I can whisper 'I love you' in your ear
Where you say you love me too!
Where you kiss me with such passion
Anything less would never do
I close my eyes and I feel you pressed against me
Our bodies move in a primal rhythm
No matter how hard we try, how close we get
We never fill the chasm
We are at the edge, but we hold on
To make love a little longer
I didn't want to fall in love with you
I only wish my heart were stronger

Dragon Slayer

When I was younger,
I had a dream of how my life would be.
Strong arms holding me tight, loving words,
whispered just for me.

All would be right in my world.

But as I grew up and became an adult,
my dream became a nightmare.
The monster searched me out, chasing,
leaving me in constant fear.

All would be chaos in my world.

But I found my strength, I found my courage,
stared the monster in the eye.
I grabbed my sword; I slew that dragon.
And I held his head up high.

All is peaceful in my world.

Dear Diary

It happened again today.
I saw him and my heart was all a flutter.
My eyes are drawn to him,
like they have a mind of their own.
Did he look at me too?
Will he ever see me?
How I would love if he would notice me.
If he took me in his arms and kissed me so
passionately that my knees got weak.
Then he would have to hold me tighter.
Just the thought....
That could happen.
Tonight, I'll wish on a star.
That he will see me and like what he sees.
That he would want me like I want him.
I'll speak with intention, my wish out to the universe.
But until my wish is granted, I can only tell you.
Thank you for being such a good friend Diary.
I know my secrets are always safe with you.

Closed Doors

Behind closed doors is where we can be ourselves.
Holding.
Touching.
Just you and me.
When you hold me in your arms,
My body comes alive.
Your hands work magic on my skin.
Touching so lightly, causing gooseflesh to rise.
My skin getting warmer with each caress.
Your lips on mine stoke the flame your hands have
ignited.
With our tongues at war, hands finding our favorite
places,
Passion takes us over the edge.
We give in to the craving.
We love soft.
We love hard.
We love deeply.
We love each other.
Every day.
Behind closed doors.

Breathe

I know I am in love with you
and I know I'm not supposed to
But there are just some things that are out of my
control

I love you for who you are
just because you are you
It's like you're the missing piece of me that makes me
whole

I pray one day you'll feel the same
that you might love me too
All I can do now is just breathe
cause you're so deep inside my soul

.

Bloom

My heart is full, and I feel like I can conquer anything.
Is this how the rose feels when it blooms?
When its petals open, is this how freedom feels?
Freedom to fly like the birds, soaring to new heights?
Finally letting go?
Taking the leap,
trusting myself,
and the universe?
And if I start to fall, hoping to be caught and held on
to, so I'd never hurt again?

Yes!
I will soar to the moon and to the stars.
Collecting the beams and stardust as I pass by.
Finding my sparkle,
my shine,
my glory.
Shining so brightly that the darkness runs and hides.
Fear of being singed and burned.
Never to come back again.

Yes.
It's my time to bloom.
It's my time to soar.
It's my time to shine.

Branding You Mine

As we lay here spent from a night of unbridled sex,
I wonder how much longer you will stay.
How soon before you leave and go home to her?
And I can't help but wonder,
do you hide the love bites I leave on your skin,
branding you mine?
Does she notice the scratches where my nails dig into
your flesh, from when you made my body shudder
with waves of pleasure?
Does she taste my sweet nectar on your lips from
when you fed between my legs?
Or does she only see you in the dark?
Tell me.
I need to know.

Acceptance

And I stood there looking at you,
really looking at you.
And it dawned on me I am seeing who you really are
for the first time.
I see the sparkle in your eyes, the glow on your face,
a softness in your features.
I vaguely remember seeing them before.

And you're staring back at me, really looking at me.
You see the smile spreading across my lips,
my light getting brighter.
And I begin to radiate with a love I have never felt
before.
I close my eyes and bask in the moment while I take it
all in.

And as I looked back in the mirror,
I finally found acceptance.
I've learned to love myself again.

About Charlene Fox

Charlene was born and raised in a suburb south of Detroit Michigan. Of five daughters, Charlene was the artistic one who loved crafts, painting, and poetry. She started writing as a hobby in high school and stopped in her 20's when 'life got in the way'. After a long hiatus she started hitting the computer keys in 2021 as a way of healing from her abusive past and sharing a part of her story on the website CUT19 with the hope that anyone suffering from abuse who saw her words would know they are not alone.

Throughout 2022 Charlene has stepped outside her comfort zone and continued to write many forms of poetry and prose about love and relationships and has had several of her pieces published in three anthologies this year; 'Trails of Light', 'A Touch of Temptation' and 'Love is Helpless'.

Charlene still resides in her hometown with her rescue cat Halfpint.

To read more of her writing you can find her on Facebook at facebook.com/charlenesclosetofthoughts and on Instagram at @cfoxpoetry.

Made in the USA
Monee, IL
04 February 2023

27124057R00095